CONVERGENCE

CONVERGENCE

A LITERARY ARTS JOURNAL
OF THE
SAVANNAH COLLEGE OF ART AND DESIGN

EDITED BY

JOHN VALENTINE
TERESA GRIFFIS

Savannah College of Art and Design

The editors are very grateful to Paula Rowan,
president of the Savannah College of Art and Design,
for her continuous support of this project.
Convergence would not have been possible without her.

The editors would also like to thank Janice Shay,
Cameron Spencer and Winslett Long at Design Press
for their untiring efforts in designing and
producing *Convergence*.

Special thanks to Scott Boylston for his help in selecting
artwork for *Convergence*, and to Dick Krepel for
providing the cover image.

Marilyn Nelson's, Cathy Smith Bowers's and Bin Ramke's appearance in
Convergence is sponsored by the writing minor program of the Savannah College
of Art and Design and the Georgia Poetry Circuit.

"Wild Pansies" and "Dusting" are reprinted by permission of Louisiana
State University Press from *The Fields of Praise: New and Selected Poems*, by
Marilyn Nelson. Copyright © 1997 by Marilyn Nelson.

"Learning How to Pray" and "Slow" are reprinted by permission of Iris
Books from *Traveling in Time of Danger* by Cathy Smith Bowers.
Copyright © 1999 by Cathy Smith Bowers.

"Captains of Default" was first published in *The Missouri Review*
(Vol XIX, #1) in 1996.

Published by Design Press
The name Design Press and the logo are trademarks of
the Savannah College of Art and Design

SAN: 2 5 3 - 4 6 5 7
Copyright © 2000 by Design Press
ISBN 1-893974-15-4
Library of Congress Card Number: 00-109818

CONTENTS

J ust as most of our experience is a confluence of word and image, Convergence, the literary arts magazine for the Savannah College of Art and Design, is dedicated to presenting a spectrum of excellent written and visual work. This publication features the selected work of talented writers and artists who work at the college, as well as that of alumni, and three poets who visited during the 1999–2000 academic year under the auspices of the Georgia Poetry Circuit. We are grateful to our contributors for sharing with us their alluring visions and words.

PERSONAL

Dear Northern European, 25, of blue eyes, blond hair, very attractive and intelligent:

I was very much taken with your ad in the *Houston Press*, March 19–25. Since I like tennis (squash too), arts (literary, film, photographic), travel (South Seas), books (poetry, fiction, nonfiction), I decided to send the requested photo. Of what you did not specify, so I chose one of my favorites, a picture of several elephants in India charging a depot of rum casks, which only the day before they had raided with impunity. This time armed guards await their charge. Since I have not sent a photograph of myself you cannot but think I do not pass muster on the "very handsome" requirement, but if I were to assure you, with or without photographic proof, that I am *in fact quite handsome*, you might not help thinking that I was vain, and that would lead to a misunderstanding before we even had the occasion to meet. To be frank, I don't *have* a picture of myself that I would send through the mail, but because I found your ad so appealing, I thought I'd write anyway, and in the meanwhile have a picture taken and send it soon.

My livelihood is nuclear physics (college), my avocation, writing (a book forthcoming, *Black Holes*, articles in *Scientific American*, *Journal of Physics*, etc.) and I think it would be great good fun if you would acknowledge this letter with a photo of your own—not of yourself, unless you'd like—but of a favorite building perhaps, a Polaroid of your tennis racket, a postcard from a museum, or a picture of a place you've traveled to and loved and want to return to someday.

Awaiting your reply,

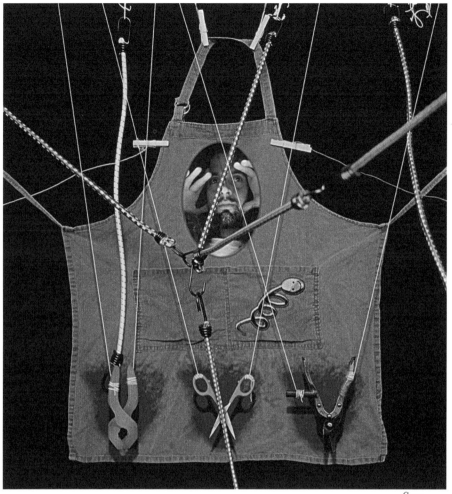

Greg
STEVE BLISS

Dear Northern European, of blue eyes, blond, intelligent, and very attractive:

Here is the photograph you requested. Of what part of my person you did not specify, but I assume you wanted a photograph of my face—not my elbow or backside—so here are two slightly out-of-focus, photobooth snapshots, which at the Galleria Mall drop out of the machine in a dandy, though moist, strip, next to the skating rink, west side, ground floor. Two bucks for four poses. What you now possess are the most passable of two attempts. In the others I'm smiling outright, but I thought I looked a bit ridiculous (smiling at whom?), so I apologize in advance if these, well, look too *serious*. I have a splendid sense of humor, more than enough to laugh at myself just now when I realize, not for the first time since I decided to answer your ad, that I am writing to a woman I have never met, wanting one moment to explain that though my hairline is cropped in these shopping mall snapshots no, *I am not bald,* and the next wanting to convey my magnanimity and genius and good sense with a clever turn of phrase, talking to this stranger through an ad in a free arts and entertainment rag and a post office box across a distance that could be two blocks or forty miles, all with an anticipation that she will read this and be amused and intrigued that I, among others, responded. I imagine you too sifting through these letters alone or with friends, at turns amazed, confused, interested, frightened, as often as not sent into fits of hysterical laughter. . . .Who does this guy think he *is* . . . look at *this* one.

I am a "WM," as you can see, 43 years old, and very much divorced. Please write.

Sincerely,

Dear blue-eyed Northern European,

The postal service is not, as far as I know, on strike, and not receiving a response, but expecting one nonetheless, I decided to write again. I saw your ad again in this week's *Houston Press* (third consecutive week) and wonder why you take so long to answer your letters. Have you been ill? If so, I hope you are feeling better now. A dreadful bug has been going around—high fever, vomiting, swollen joints, diarrhea—and yesterday close to half my students (58) were absent from my introductory lecture on nuclear fusion. Did you know the sun is a giant fusion reactor? Enclosed is a picture of the atomic mushroom, the first detonation of a thermonuclear bomb, "The Mike," on November 1, 1952, at Eniwetok in the Marshal Islands, using nuclear fission, of course. I'd like to travel there someday and seek out the crater it left, half a mile deep and two miles wide.

May I recommend *The Making of the Atomic Bomb*?

Sincerely,

Dear blue-eyed blond Northern European:

Are you chaste? Are you fair? Is your name Astarte? Are you a Dane? Is your name Diana? Shall I celebrate the moon goddess feast with cider, a roasted goat spitted on hazel branches and apples hanging from a bough?

Dear blond blue-eyes of the North:

I had a dream last night. You wore pelts and leather thongs and carried a javelin carved from blackened oak. The world had ended in blistering winds; darkness fell over the land; we lived in a cave, hoarding fruit and water, and made love in the deep night beneath a moon shrouded in ash. In the northern cold a sword of fire opened the sky, and we watched the whorl of the Milky Way.

Dear Northern European,

Your ad appeared again this week. How goes it? I suspect you have not yet gotten back from the developers the picture(s) you plan on sending. With the collapse of communism we have only deranged sentries at nuclear silos to fear. Have you seen *Dr. Strangelove*? An improbable scenario, but the film had a profound effect on me, an impressionable teen of the ripening Sixties. Do you know the real reason Truman dropped Fat Man on Hiroshima? The scientists on the Manhattan Project who developed the atomic bomb wanted to see how much havoc their beautiful invention would wreak. Enclosed is a photograph of the Nagasaki hypocenter. Do you like rum? I do, lately, ice-cold, up.

Dear Northern European, of blue eyes, blond, and most attractive:

Doubtless you are surprised to receive this letter at your home address. How did I get it? Student hackers, Internet. No one is safe anymore. You are indeed very attractive, and blond, with turquoise, aquamarine, breathtaking South Sea blue eyes (I stood next to you in produce while you weighed in your hand various heads of lettuce, and caught you looking at me in the reflecting mirrors above the vegetables, with a shade of annoyance, I thought; I stood too close?), though I cannot yet vouch for your intelligence; given your listlessness as a pen pal, one wonders, as I do with many of my students, if you are able even to read. I have taken my own photographs of you, in fact. Do you mind?

Sincerely,

Dear European:

With the bomb we brought the sun to the earth. We all steal fire, do we not? We imagine we're safe—we have to, don't we—but do you know there is madness on this land? The cold war is long over, but soon we will have warm wars and then very hot wars. Eventually even the sun will explode, devouring the planets it gave birth to.

Dear Northern European, of blue eyes, blond, intelligent, and very attractive:

Today in my office I was visited by a Harris County Sheriff, who informed me that an injunction against my person had been placed by the white goddess. I am not allowed to come within fifty feet of your most attractive blondness, under threat of confiscation of computer files and hard drives. No matter. Your name is Irene, *Er-e*-nay in north Europa, but here in Texas, *Ah*-rene.

Dear Ahrene,

I am the sound of the sea. I am a battle-waging spear. Who makes clear the ruggedness of the mountains? Who but myself knows where the sun sets? Who foretells the ages of stone? I am a griffin on a cliff, a fire of the sun. I am a wild oar in water, a winnowing fan ashore. On whom do the willows sigh?

Hazel, yew, holly, eucalyptus. Willow wand, apple tree. I am a wide flood on a plain, a wind on the deep waters, the threatening noise of the sea. Who but I knows the secret of the unhewn oak?

Dear Irene,

As a child I was verbally abused, mostly by afternoon television. Poor Mother was an addict. *As the World Turns, Guiding Light, Queen for a Day.* Thank God she died before the invention of talk shows. However, I did not. Do you know how difficult it is for me to accept rejection? I had a calculus professor in college whose wife divorced him; soon he took to wearing a hard hat in class and out, day and night; the sky was falling. Many possible reactions to rejection are possible: sorrow; a cruise with Rush Limbaugh or John Bradshaw, depending on one's temperament; masturbation; travel; binge drinking; prayer; hospitalization. What will I opt for? Wearing a hard hat feels a bit extreme.

Enclosed are some choice telephotos of you riding your roller blades in Memorial Park. I trust the gentleman who accompanied you is not an unhappy acquaintance made through the same ad to which I responded so sincerely? I thought not.

Dear Barbarian of the Northland:

Enclosed are some photographs of your beau entering and exiting an adult bookstore. He is either a pervert or driven to despair by your coy refusals. Perhaps you sent him on an errand into that wilderness to rent a pornographic movie or purchase a g-string and feather boa for your new employ. In Houston there are scores of men's clubs where young women are handsomely compensated by businessmen for a naked terpsichore. I went to one, once. For weeks afterward every time I saw a

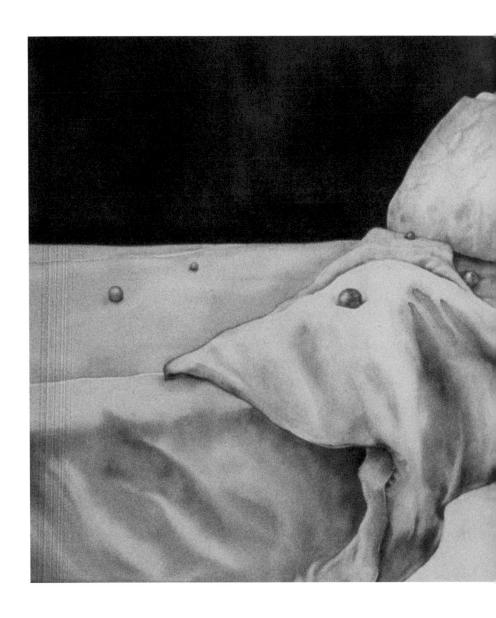

young woman, I wanted to ask her, Are you a topless dancer? Thousands upon thousands in *Houston*, the first syllables uttered from the moon. College girls. Middle-class. Clean, nice girls who need money for school or a BMW.

Young women everywhere in *Houston, the Eagle has landed*, many of them topless dancers, who work as "showgirls" in what are known as *titty bars*, or *titty joints*. One day we'll colonize Neptune, Io, Venus, Pluto,

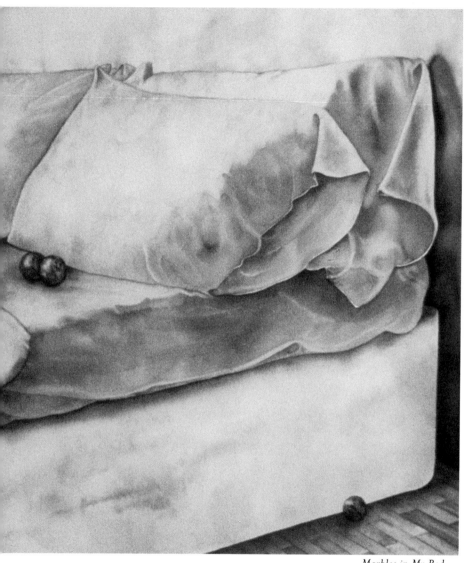

Marbles in My Bed
JOY L. FLYNN

each with women, some of them lap dancers. Which ones are, which ones are not? Do breast implants weigh much? Thousands of jell packs under thousands of lights making tens of thousands for thousands of girls in Houston. Are *you* a topless dancer? Where do you work? I'd like to buy a lap dance. Can you explain your boyfriend entering and exiting an adult bookstore? Twenty-five is not yet over the hill for table dancing. Not by a long shot.

Dear N.E.,

I write today—I wrote yesterday—knowing you would not receive the first epistle by the time I penned the second.

Given the erotomania of America—politicians, preachers, no one is exempt—do you think it's possible that a bomb pack, a Minuteman, an ICBM, might spontaneously explode from the subtle vibrations of satellite signals? MTV alone might start a firestorm.

In my garage I am building a gift for you, a sacrifice. Rum drunk for two weeks. Classes cancelled. I call it Irene. She is the daughter of Themis, a Titaness who by some accounts gave birth to Prometheus. Themis, mother of the Horae, who showers the earth with life-giving rain. Thallo, flower-bearer; Carpo, bearer of fruit. Eunomia, goddess of order. Dice, goddess of justice. And Irene, goddess of peace. One of Aphrodite's minions, who adorns her hair with passion flowers, water lilies, snapdragons. Sisters to the Fates, the inevitable fates. Irene: goddess of peace. Peacekeeper.

>—+—+>—0—<+—+—<

Untitled
BEN MORRIS

WILD PANSIES

for Mandy Jordan

I rested in my mother's womb,
a lily on the pond.
Gentle waves moved the water;
I rocked, held by a twisted cord
of roots.
From the moment I was planted there
I thought about learning to walk
more than nine months
before I was born.

I listened to the voices
of the water around me;
sometimes I thought a storm
was really three hearts
beating as one.

I grew from a bundle of jelly-eggs
into a tadpole nosing the water weeds.
Then I was the size of a rainbow trout,
and then I was me.

I jumped up the falls
of the birth canal
and knew, as my body
hit sunlight,
what it would feel like to fly.
But when I got to the top
I could breathe water no more.

Before I drew dry air
for the first time
into my lungs,
I said to myself, Remember.

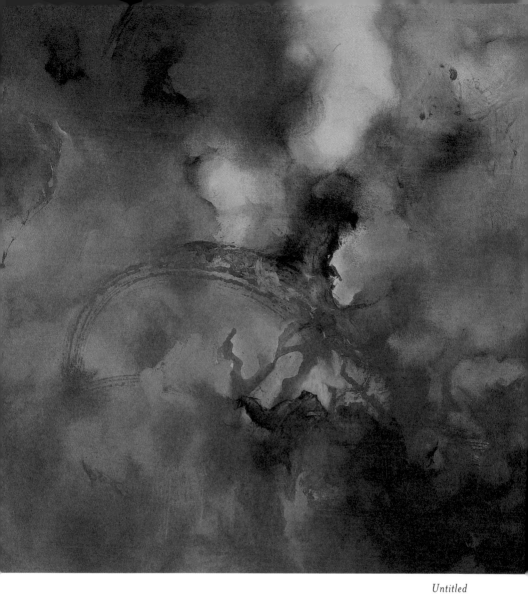

Untitled
TARA MCKIERNAN

How the pine trees
shadowed the water
when evening came.
How the sunset was reflected.
How the wild pansies
grew along the shore.

DUSTING

Thank you for these tiny
particles of ocean salt,
pearl-necklace viruses,
winged protozoans:
for the infinite,
intricate shapes
of submicroscopic
living things.

For algae spores
and fungus spores,
bonded by vital
mutual genetic cooperation,
spreading their
inseparable lives
from equator to pole.

My hand, my arm,
make sweeping circles.
Dust climbs the ladder of light.
For this infernal, endless chore,
for these eternal seeds of rain:
Thank you. For dust.

Pantheon
WINSLETT LONG

CAPTAINS BY DEFAULT

The snow is delicate and knee high. It is cotton candy in my mouth, too fleeting to satisfy but enjoyable just the same. I bend in midstride and shovel the powder with my gloved hand. With this motion I leave a smooth and straight gully that strikes me as the most perfect consequence of my effort, conspicuous in its complete lack of fault. I pack the snow against the roof of my mouth and suck it of its moisture. The remains trickle down my throat.

We trudge over the white curves of the golf course in tempered anticipation, led by Brad. His shin pads thrust forward and spoil the chaste evenness of the snow as clots of it roll across the surface with each footstep. Brad is like his father, neither tall nor short. His broad shoulders buttress a head of dirty-blond hair and keen eyes. The eyes are steadily indifferent, the hair as straight as his stance. When we play dibble in the lake, the stick is most often found in Brad's grasp.

Behind him, Tim concentrates with narrow diligence on the impressions left by Brad. He is smaller than Brad in every way. He walks with his head down and his eyes rapt on the heels in front of him. His is the pursuit of a disciple, convinced of salvation through emulation. He follows Brad this way through grass and mud as well as snow.

The pond is a smudge in the distance. It borders a brief but dense wood that stands like an oasis upon the sculpted rolls of the course. It is a rectangular basin with steep, powder-packed banks that serve us well as backboards. On the far corner is a pump that runs year-round, in a small wooden shed, isolated on its perch. On one side it is braced by a thicket of evergreen and on the other side by the tar-black water it refuses to let freeze. Its influence reaches ten feet in each direction, the resulting hole the only blemish on the otherwise smooth ice. There is no desire within our group to explore the monotonous groans and darkened windows of the pump house or the lightless hole it creates in the ice. It is never mentioned between us.

I am third in line. I follow without the thought of being led. The terrain of the golf course is as familiar to me as the musty crawl space that extends from the cellar of my house. I recognize slouching firs that have sheltered trenched and tunneled forts stocked with snowball grenades and icicle

Brian
PETE CHRISTMAN

rations, sand traps that have served as bunkers in warmer weather, and broad oaks and maples that still hold skeletal remains of meticulously built tree forts attended to more during their construction than any time after. This familiarity has not tarnished my intrigue but has allowed it to prosper.

Stan and Ian Finch walk in unison behind me. They are often mistaken for twins. The actual discrepancy in years is secreted by their equal eagerness to please, just as a retriever and her grown pup can appear to be from the same litter. They are not bothered by this, not even Stan, the elder of the two, but relish the low profile and anonymity of sharing an identity. Halloween finds them draped in matching white sheets. They have eye holes and slits for their mouths that are smeared with chocolate and spit. They have been ghosts for several years and have no complaints.

Each winter we vow to recover the countless pucks that slap into the inky water like skipping stones before finally nosediving, or skid to the brink at a taunting crawl only to slip over the edge just at the moment we thought they would stop. We joke that soon an island of black rubber will rise from the murky water like a volcano, and we will make a fortune selling the black discs by the truckload. But by spring's resurgence we have other crusades in mind.

We each bring two pucks—the oldest ones we can find—pocked with misuse on summer-heated asphalt. If luck accompanies us out, and we do not lose all of our pucks, we play until the scarcity of light assigns all objects the same color, then we reluctantly retrace our path in the moonglow. We are careful not to pass too close to the wooded areas where shadows from the creaking branches hang like webs on the blue surface of the snow. We still harbor the fears of childhood, after all. The journey back may take minutes or hours, interrupted by tussles or snow angel exhibitions or lying on our backs watching our own huffs of breath against the velvet sky. We are each the last soul on earth then. We move only with regret, urged by a tingling of our backsides and the inevitable tickling itch growing around our feet that will stay with us long after the warmth of home has chased away the cold from our bodies.

Virgil trails the pack by several yards. If not for his sheer inability to brave the untrodden snow without quickly losing pace, he would set his own course. He is stronger in mind than in body. His insistence that the pond can be reached more quickly by first walking farther north on the road rather than trekking directly across the contours of the blanketed course falls on deaf ears. We cross this way because the rest of us agree with Brad when he says it is more fun to create your own trail. Virgil's disinclination is worn on his face and posture. He drags his equipment behind him, like a dog on a leash, through the snow. Virgil's opinions, no matter how vehemently conveyed, encourage scorn from Brad and wary disregard from the rest of us. He is mouselike with a red nose that runs with things better left unseen. His hair is matted as if he has just taken off a baseball cap for the first time in weeks. His appearance is irksome. His demeanor, in response to our continuous dismissal, has grown to match his appearance.

Virgil refuses to shoulder his equipment-clad hockey stick, and his skates occasionally clank in protest. He breathes heavily, martyred. We weave through the concealed hazards of the golf course behind Brad like a row of railway cars. We cross the open spaces as soldiers on the march, fully armed, our weapons slung cocksure over our shoulders. Our feet squeak in near unison on the snow. We are Washington's men at Valley Forge, Napoleon's troops before Waterloo, Snow White's six dwarfs with Grumpy at the rear rubbing his runny nose and dragging his shovel all the way. The brittle cold brings sharp sensation into our lungs and pinches our nostrils. Stillness whistles past, and we breathe like dragons.

When we reach the pond we sit on our jackets and lace up. The jackets remain on rest stops and penalty seats. We dress in our heroes' jerseys and rarely match our teammates. Stan and Ian are the exception. There are no goalies, no defensemen, no left wings, right wings or centers; there are only hockey players. We shoot for the space between our opponents' discarded boots. Over the bank is over the crossbar. To compensate for the dark pool of unfrozen water, we swing our boots toward the opposite corner.

We rarely lose a puck to the snow that surrounds the pond, and we never moan when one breaches the shallow crest. Instead there is a hysterical rush to the hidden puck and whoever recovers it is rewarded with a goal. We charge the bank, glide for a step and then, with eyes wide, we leap, knees or head first, diving into the snow and digging like mad. There are days when a thin and fragile layer of ice coats the snow and the puck leaves a telltale hole where it lands. These frenzied quests provide us with a tension breaker from our game, which we play with the violence if not the skill or talent of our idols. Tempers flare, and with them gloves and sticks fly.

I am captain by default. Tim will not willingly oppose Brad who, again by default, albeit one of a different kind, is captain of the other side. Stan and Ian refuse to step forward. Virgil is pushed back whenever he tries. I am fortified by the Finch brothers, invariably a package deal. Virgil is teamed with Brad and Tim. We play the best of five games and win because Virgil is ignored by his teammates.

We do not have periods but break on mutual exhaustion. Snow provides nourishment. We take it in slowly, wary of the dull ache that too much cold at one time will invite. We wipe past the top layers and dig into the virgin snow and bring the precious mound to our faces slowly so that none of the powder is lost. We lap at it with the hope that just once we will get more than we already know we will get. It feels good to lie still and we lob snow at each other in lazy arcs, laughing and coughing up the cold air.

Our game starts up again slowly with the more eager rising to skate in shiftless circles with a puck or ice chunk bouncing between the wooden blades of their sticks. We shuffle teammates so that I have Virgil and Tim, and the Finch brothers are with Brad. It is ancient law that Brad and I never side on the same team. It goes unsaid and unquestioned.

With the new alignment Tim pauses indiscriminately, as if Virgil has just stepped onto the ice. There is no sign of the scorn so venomously exhibited in the first games. Without Brad's influence, Virgil becomes a competent teammate in Tim's eyes. In fact, Virgil and Tim share a certain tenacity, as well as an unspoken appreciation for each other's manic drive to prove themselves. They are more like each other than either knows, or would admit. We lose ourselves in the game, breathing heavily and finding that our lungs expand in compensation. There is a freshness at the bottom of them.

Tim passes the puck in my direction, but Brad, sensing Tim's intentions, cuts between the two of us and skates at full speed toward our goal. Only Virgil is between Brad and the net, and he skates backward watching Brad's eyes. He is awkward but firm in his motion. Brad is capable of quickly getting the puck past Virgil, his wrist shot is hard and sure, but instead he thrusts forward and engages Virgil. There is a collision, but not of the sort we expect. Virgil is not flattened. Instead, the blade of his stick deftly slaps the puck away and then inadvertently slips between the stanchions of Brad's skates. Brad falls immediately onto his stomach and slides toward the snowbank. The brunt of the impact is absorbed by his head. There is a faint crunch and then silence as the rest of us skate to a halt.

The brief hush is shattered by mirth at the sight of Brad as he turns his head, nostrils packed with snow. The force of the blow has driven both his eyelids upward, and he wears a dazed smile. He blows a snow pellet from his nostril and we laugh again, but Brad is unaccustomed to this side of mockery. There is another short silence as he unsteadily rises to his skates and shakes his head free of snow, nearly losing his balance. This is too much for us. Tim slips and falls to the ice he is laughing so hard. Stan

Railroad Overpass
Sandra Reed

and Ian fall into a snowbank. Virgil smiles meekly and allows his body to
sag in amusement.

We all look away from Brad momentarily, so no one sees him rush
headlong toward Virgil. Before anyone knows what is happening he buries
his shoulder into Virgil's chest. We watch him fall to the ice and curl up
in pain, the breath knocked out of him. Brad skates back to where his stick
has fallen and swoops to pick it up without stopping. There is no sound
other than the methodical ripping of Brad's blades on the ice as he skates
back toward Virgil. He wears a dubious grin we all have seen, not knowing
if it reflects leniency or retribution. He glides to Virgil, who is still trying
to get his breath, and hooks the blade of his stick between one of his
skates. He circles him slowly so that Virgil spins on his back like a top.
The apparently benign retort settles the rest of us and we chuckle at the
sight. Virgil relaxes somewhat and plays along.

After several turns Brad straightens his line and tows Virgil around
the pond. He turns and then turns again so that the two of them make a
figure eight. We applaud the performance. The relief and appreciation of

being a part of something shows on Virgil's face. He has almost forgotten the pain in his chest. They are a figure skating team. Brad goes into a tight spin and Virgil revolves around him like a satellite. There are cheers from the rest of us. Brad again breaks out of the formation and then skates to the corner furthest from the pump house and its dark moat. He pauses in the corner as if preparing to make his final pass. Brad takes a bow, careful to keep his stick high enough to prevent Virgil from freeing his foot. Uncertainty fills my stomach like syrup. Brad throws a complicit glance toward Tim, whose face quickly drains of amusement. He rises and skates toward the two and smiles with a plea. No words pass between anyone, as if we all know our roles. Brad nods toward Virgil's other skate. Tim obeys his unspoken command and hooks Virgil's free skate with his own stick. We titter as if to assure Brad that he need not take the threat any further; he is in control once again. He tips his head toward the quivering water and looks into Tim's eyes. They fuzz like cataracts.

They are forty feet away from the unfrozen area and picking up speed. Brad and Tim are on either side of Virgil, who is spread-eagle between them like the contents of a slingshot. The last hint of uneasy laughter is swallowed by the sound of steel edges cutting ice. Stan and Ian look at each other and then down to their feet. I stand when they are twenty feet away. I hope the motion alone will distract them and bring them back. Of course, it does not. Tim has abandoned his glances toward Brad and is staring ahead now in vacant obedience.

I skate into their path and yell Brad's name, but I am not there for him. The frigid pool is behind me; I am at its edge. I hear the hum of the pump, and the patient lapping of the water. I take two strides and jump at Brad. My shoulder hits him in the stomach and he leaves his feet as I push him down to the ice with a resounding crack. I think to myself that it is a good hit. I land on top of him. In one motion he rolls on top of me, punches me in the face and stands, but he is hurt. He holds his gut and bends over in pain. He skates away, laughing under his breath.

Tim, still holding Virgil by the skate, comes to a stop two feet away from the edge of the ice. There is guilt about him, then quick anger, like I spoiled his fun. He skates by and mutters an obscenity as I lie on the ice with blood dripping from my nose. He follows Brad to their boots and begins unlacing his skates. Brad already has his skates off and is bending over in pain. He continues laughing as both of them walk off the ice and into the barren landscape. They follow the same course that led them here. Brad walks in our footprints and Tim pushes through untrodden snow directly beside him. I look back at Virgil, but he watches each one of us without expression. We are accomplices, witnesses, one no better than the other. Our silence is our guilt. Ian's eyes have not left the ground, Stan's have not left the darkening sky. I focus my attention on the stiff blood on my skin and how the caked substance cracks when I wiggle my upper lip. The air is new within my nostrils.

The Finch brothers rise and skate slowly to their boots. Not a word is spoken as they dress for their journey home. They do not look in our direction but instead throw glances at the receding figures of Brad and Tim. Then they are up and off with a feeble acknowledgment. They walk at a slow and deliberate pace to the path and then speed up in random spurts. They run for several strides and then slow back down, almost in unison. As they move further from the pond the sprints come more frequently until they are almost galloping through the snow, plowing ahead like dogs after their master.

I come very close to laughing at the sight of Virgil. His nose is as red as I've ever seen it. He follows the progression of the Finch brothers with narrow eyes, and then lifts himself and skates past me. I think he does not realize I am there as his skate blade comes within inches of my bare hand. I know I will not move until he leaves or says something. I have no desire to speak a word to him, and I dread to hear his voice. I watch the dark ripples make their way across the flat water and bump harmlessly into the stark whiteness of ice. The pump is like a heartbeat; it drones despite the cold, despite everything. I feel as if the island of black rubber is about to emerge, as dark and still and cold as the water that conceals it. I pay no attention as Virgil makes his way across the golf course. He does not follow the others, but cuts directly across toward the road somewhere off through the trees. His progress is slow, and laborious, and irrefutable. He becomes a dot in the distance like the rest of them.

I stand and skate toward the snowbank that holds my belongings. I sit, remove my skates and rub the sleepy tingle from my feet. It is a wonderful feeling. The sun is nearly absent. It seeps through dark trees on the horizon. I walk home over untrodden snow, and go out of my way to avoid our old trails. As the last glow of sun thins to purple I fall into the snow and lie still and listen to the empty creaking of winter.

>-+◆>-◦-◆+-◄

LES DEMOISELLES

after Picasso

I too want to be stripped
of even my form, to lie among layers
of paint, cream and pearl,
hung from a nail
at the Museum of Modern Art.

From my Iberian, Babylonian, African mothers,
from the ancient spike of my heel,
spill of my stocking–
wiped up–
spilled again–
I offer six views of one breast–
Feast!

Untitled
PAUL SABO

Limerick Lady
DENISE FALK

RAW ANGELS

We waltzed on plains
that opened
to a slow jazz of wind,
whirled to the ancient wail
of a dissolving moon,
translucent and wet,
a raw angel that dripped
through you to me.
We lay in the long memory
of a riverbed—
I kissed you back
to your birth,
to the original wound
where you swirled off
on an eddy
of thin blue.
I was the color of new seeds
rising like the sun
to the surface
of this bare earth,
luminous dust
luminous dust
I track lightly now
into the lives
of other men.

Adoration
SHELLEY DAVIS

MEETIN'

Elijah and Mary Jones closed the crudely hewn oak door, stepped across a narrow platform serving as a porch, and descended the twelve wooden steps to the damp, soft ground. Their cabin was situated upon eight pilings cut from oak trees as marsh dwellings had to be in order to weather storms and high tides. The cabin was in a small clearing cut out of the thick trees, brush and lush greenery of the island's western extremity. The island was about two miles long north to south, and one mile or so wide. The eastern bank was bordered by a wide river across which lay marsh with its waving savannah grass traversed and crossed by smaller streams. Beyond this wide expanse were two more islands, barriers before the ocean. To the west of the island, running north and south, ran a smaller river called Thomas Creek. Marsh with smaller streams composed the remainder of the island's periphery.

Elijah and Mary were going toward Thomas Creek from the cabin, which was set back about two hundred yards from the bank. As Mary negotiated the last step, Elijah reached his long, muscular arm to her. He was a large man, six feet-two inches tall, strong, and very black. The squared features of his face and his straight, proud carriage gave him an imposing, regal look. He wore his black wool pants and coat, a homemade cotton shirt, and black boots.

Mary, who took his hand and stepped to the ground, was also large. She was strong and well-proportioned. Her complexion was lighter than Elijah's with some Caucasian influence in her nose and light-colored eyes. She wore a tight-fitting cotton dress that had come from town. It was her best, and it went well with her dyed white shoes, also from town. Elijah's eyes were drawn to her cleavage, which became evident as she stepped down.

"Eli, what are you lookin' at? You see plenty of me, and now you have that look—"

"You look good, Mary."

"Besides, we're goin' to meetin'."

"Meetin's your doin', Mary; I just go along."

They were walking through a wooded path from the cabin to the river. "I know, Eli, but this is a special one; I know it. I had dreams—"

"Your dreams, Mary—"

The Heads of Head #1
ELETHIA OLIVER-AJOSE

Mary stopped abruptly. "Shhush, Eli. Stop!" They stood motionless and quiet as a doe and a several-month-old fawn appeared from the green onto the path a few steps ahead of them. The deer stopped, turning their heads toward the people. Elijah's eyes went to Mary's, which were wide and mobile, then forward to the gazes of the deer. The force between the eyes of the deer and Mary was electric. Elijah saw Mary's eyes fixed, yet he recognized a flash of eroticism that he treasured. Slowly the deer crossed the path and went into the thick, green growth on the other side. The doe looked back—straight at Mary before disappearing.

Elijah wondered at this quick experience. They walked in silence to the bank of the river. The tide was in; the water was practically at their feet. Had it been low tide, they would have had to carry or drag the boat across several hundred yards of mud, grass, and oysters to the river. Elijah untied the boat from a tree, pulled it to the bank, and pushed it into the water. It was a rowboat about fourteen feet long with a board aft and one slightly forward of center for sitting when one was able to sit. Elijah put the two oars in and a long pole. It was in this boat that he made his living, often on this river. He situated Mary on the rear seat, and he sat on the forward seat facing her. He fit the oars into the oarlocks and began rowing with smooth easy strokes. Two splashes from a long limb extending from shore caused neither of them to look; they recognized the sound of turtles dropping into the water. He watched their cabin grow smaller and disappear as his companion looked across the river to the large Green Island which, along with the greenish blue of the water and the blue sky, comprised her view.

Mary felt the alternating rhythm of the morning sun's rays and shadows from the towering cypress and oak trees as the boat moved through the water. She smiled as a dragonfly flew through one of the rays. Elijah turned the boat south. The river was slowly winding southwest around Green Island to her left. Only the quiet stroking of the oars offered response to the occasional cries of birds. As the boat rounded the bend, the river narrowed, and Elijah steered near the overgrown shore to stay with the channel. Mary's eyes widened at a commotion just ahead on shore. She straightened and strained to look. Elijah stopped rowing and turned to see. They could hear splashing and vaguely see turmoil in the water.

Elijah spoke. "See—there in the shallow, the heron."

At first Mary could not see the blue heron. Then, as though it just appeared, she saw it.

"Oh, Eli, look." The blue heron was thrusting its head atop its long neck straight up and shaking all over in six to eight inches of water. Its beak was clamped onto a wriggling snake about two or three feet long. The heron stepped onto land, dropped the snake and pecked it, picked it up, still writhing, dropped it, pecked some more until it lay motionless. The bird then clamped onto its kill, flew to the top limb of a cypress, tightened its grip and flew into the sunlight.

The two sat silently. Elijah, the river man who had seen much of nature's show, continued to stare after the vanished bird.

"That bird got himself a snake."

He turned back to Mary and saw her transfixed gaze. An indiscernible utterance emanated from her lips, a language, but not his. Slowly she returned his look. Her visage regained the intense, erotic look he recalled from the encounter with the deer. Her face softened.

"Sure did, Eli. You never know." In deep thought Elijah settled into his rowing position; Mary also shifted and got more comfortable. The river rounded the island and opened into a larger river, the Big River, running west to east eventually to the Atlantic Ocean. The other side of the Big River at this point was a half mile away. Elijah rowed turning west, staying as close to shore as possible. They passed a ramshackle shack where Elijah did some trading when the city traders came out this far. Usually he had to travel fifteen miles upriver, most of the way to town.

"Meetin' somethin' special today, Mary?"

"I think so, Eli; feels like it. You're good to keep bringing me."

"I like seein' folks. Sometimes I like the singin'."

"I know—look!" She straightened and pointed at a canoe passing them with another couple. "Joseph, hey—Anna!"

"Mary, that you? Y'all goin' to meetin'?"

"On our way."

"See ya there."

Joseph added, "Better hurry, Eli. We're runnin' behind and passing you."

"You tell Mr. Edgar we right behind you, Joseph, and you paddle on. Almost there anyway."

After some silent rowing Mary said, "There's the dock!" Elijah guided them toward a five-foot square gray dock of uneven planking at the end of a long pier extending from shore. Several boats were tied along the dock and some along the shore; some like Elijah's, some canoes, and one flat-bottomed boat with a keel.

"There's Mr. Edgar's boat," Mary said. Elijah eased their boat into an available space, jumped onto the pier, and tied it. He then helped Mary onto the dock, and they walked along the pier toward the opening in the trees on the bank. At the end of the pier they climbed a dilapidated stair-

way up the steep bank. When they reached the top, they were fifty yards from the meetinghouse. The building was narrow, rectangular, tabby, and ground level. The door facing Elijah and Mary was of weathered oak and sheltered by a peaked shingled roof supported by two untreated cypress columns. Two windows of real glass flanked the door. Elijah opened and held the door for Mary, and they entered the meeting in progress.

They saw the backs of thirty or so standing people, all clapping and singing. They were equally distributed in front of benches placed in six rows on either side of a center aisle. A podium stood centered in front of the room with two wooden chairs behind it, empty. Behind the chairs was space, emptiness to the wall. A door was in the right corner of the front of the room. Mary and Elijah slid onto a vacant bench midway down the left side and joined in the singing. A large lady to the right of the podium was leading the singing. She wore a plain white cotton robe with a blue-fringed sash, a blue bandana on her head, and a gold-plated set of circular earrings with a matching bracelet. The singing was loud, getting louder—

Unexpected Moment
TONGJIT TIEOPHANITJAROEN

> *Ezekiel saw that wheel*
> *Way in the middle of the air.*
> *Ezekiel saw a wheel*
> *Way in the middle of the air—*

Mary joined immediately in the song, rocking side to side. Elijah too joined in the singing. He noticed that Mary had instantly attained the strength, movement and intensity of the others.

> *—big wheel run by faith*
> *An' a little wheel run by the grace of God—*

He quickly turned to look at the leader in front who, with a high-pitched yelp, began to clap and move side to side faster and faster, increasing the tempo of the song.

"Yea, Lizzy!" a voice cried out.

And another: "That's right, Lizzy!"

Elijah was amid a rhythmic movement of bobbing and swaying of stripes, solids, prints, hats, and kerchiefs. Several of the men, mostly dressed in black coats like Elijah's, were caught up in the rising pandemonium which continued to grow in volume and tempo.

"*Ezekiel saw a wheel*—" clapping, groaning, gasping—

"*Way up-uh-huh in the middle of the air*—"

"*Big wheel run by faith*—" faster, louder—

"*An' the little wheel run by the grace of God*—"

Lizzy, in front, began her voice up the scales, and the others began to trail off. "Yeah!" from behind and "Lord!" from somewhere else. She raised her arms and looked up, her voice still rising far above anything on the scales. Many in the congregation were quivering. Eyes were shut, faces turned upward with Lizzy's. Abruptly she stopped and dropped to her knees. She started through the song, she alone singing this time. She sang slower, every consonant punched while the crowd swayed and hummed. It seemed to Elijah that Mary was groaning as she moved. The perspiration was flowing in the room with a sweet pungency, a spiritual musk. The song was reaching a crescendo—everyone again joining.

"*Ezekiel saw that wheel*" (louder) "*turnin' turnin'*—"

Lizzy stopped, stood, and turned her back on the group as she faced the door which was opening. "Mr. Edgar!" someone called.

"Mr. Edgar," Elijah heard Mary utter in a voice unfamiliar to him.

Lizzy yelled as she ran to him. "Mr. Edgar!" She kissed his cheek and sat limply in one of the chairs.

Mr. Edgar walked slowly and deliberately to the podium. He was slight, about seventy with a complexion more caramel than black. His head was fringed with white hair. He wore a starched white shirt, buttoned at the neck, and a black wool suit but no tie.

He spoke: "Please sit," and before everyone was settled, he began by raising both arms and his face to the ceiling.

"Lord!" he called in a voice at once raspy and clear, and very loud. Everyone waited; he continued to look up. The electric anticipation was palpable, matched only by concentration, even Elijah's.

"Lord! Lord! Lord! Lord!" By the fifth time, each louder than the one before, the voices were joining Mr. Edgar's, "Lord! Lord—" faster and louder. Mr. Edgar's voice boomed, "Lord, hear us!" His strength quieted the others. "Does he hear us, children?"

"Yes, he hears us—"

"Yes, Mr. Edgar—"

"Um Hummmmm—"

"No!" Mr. Edgar thundered, slamming his hand to the podium.

Silence. In a lower voice he asked, "Should he? What for? I tell you God weeps; God cries out; Jesus wails for us lowly people." His voice picked up again, and as it did he began adding a syllable to the end of each word in a sentence.

"God weeps–uh. And for what–uh? I tell ya–uh. He weeps for you, children-uh. For me–uh."

Approvals, murmurings and some amens were scattered through the room.

"Yes-uh, for you-uh. You lyin'-uh, drinkin'-uh, cheatin' the trader man-uh!"

He paused, looking around. In a low voice, almost a whisper, he continued, "You need God, children. Need his grace. Need his love. Do you know where God is, children?"

"Say it, Mr. Edgar!"

"Heaven!" from another voice.

"I'm–uh tellin' you children–uh–the grace of God–is–" Mr. Edgar began to moan, swaying with arms raised. His eyes seemed to disappear. Mary squealed and Elijah started. The room seemed in motion. Lizzy joined in the swaying and began to hum "Amazing Grace." The room accompanied her. Elijah, in time with the group, looked with alarm at Mary. She was jerking convulsively, her eyes tear-filled and wide. She turned quickly to the door at the rear. Her look again frightened him. He turned to the door and saw nothing. On looking forward, he noticed Mr. Edgar staring at the door as he swayed and hummed with the group. The rear door slammed against the wall. The bang caused all to look. Two men stepped in carrying a rattan chair with an old woman scarcely taking up its space.

"Hattie!" Mary said, at first almost under her breath. "It's Hattie!" The name was repeated around the room.

"Lord," Elijah said, "I ain't even thought about her it's been so long."

Mary acknowledged his statement with a quick look, then turned. His eyes followed hers to the men carrying the chair down the middle aisle. The two men were huge. They wore overalls without shirts and walked on bare feet. The chair was plain with cotton padding dyed purple. Hattie was slight with white hair and a wrinkled black face. She had on a long red dress, simply made with a white sarong-type garment draped over one shoulder. A gold chain hung from her neck with a bright stone at the end of it, a stone that Elijah did not recognize. The bearers set the chair before Mr. Edgar and retreated to the rear.

Hattie and Mr. Edgar stared deeply into each other's eyes. She said something to him in a voice too low to be distinguishable. The intonation was strange, and as Elijah looked around, he discovered that others also shared his puzzlement. On her words Mr. Edgar slowly nodded and turned away. He walked to the corner door in the front of the room and went through it. He returned and walked to Hattie's chair carrying a staff. The staff was of mahogany and about four feet long. The head of the staff was carved and gave the appearance of a human face.

Mr. Edgar stood with the staff, looking at Hattie. He began tapping on the floor, the pattern of the taps seeming random at first; then a distinct rhythm formed, an intricate pattern of taps on the floor. The tapping got louder and faster. The wood-on-wood pattern enveloped the room. It was almost visible. As the tempo increased, sounds came from the staff that did not seem possible. The people once again began to move. A woman in front of Mary stood, her feet keeping perfect time with the beat of the staff and her shoulders rolling forward, then back. As she made her way to the front of the room, her arms rotated locomotive style with her head down. Another woman joined her, then a man. He danced stiffly yet right with the pace of the staff, raising his knees higher as he moved in more of a circle.

Mary rose and very slightly made a sound, a clicking sound; some others were making similar sounds. Mary, along with another man who had risen, worked her way to the front, dancing similarly to the others. Without missing a beat, Mr. Edgar looked closely at Hattie and returned to the podium. The rhythm of the staff changed. One relatively soft knock was followed by three very loud knocks, and a trailing down in intensity for three more thumps—then it repeated over and over. The dancers' feet beat the same pattern into the floor. All of the people, dancing or not, expelled a loud "Ho!" to the first hard hit of the staff. Everything quickened; the dancers moved at a breathtaking speed. The voices were fevered. To Elijah, the entire room was whirling. He saw sky and water, the heron shifting the snake in its mouth, the heron flying into the sun. He saw Mary's eyes and the eyes of the deer; Mr. Edgar with the staff in a flowing white robe floating in and through the tubular light. He saw Mary's skin, glistening as it did after love-making, her face looking up at him and becoming a mask, resembling dark wood and painted with a feminine face with large expressive azure eyes; then Hattie's face in a rapturous glow.

All at once Mr. Edgar, Lizzy, Hattie, and Mary uttered a simultaneous string of words never before heard by any of the company. The staff kept on as did the dancing—faster—the heat in the room continuing to rise. Elijah looked to Hattie and gasped. She was ascending from the chair. The dancers and Mr. Edgar stared with abandonment and joy, chanting and waving pointed fingers at Hattie as she continued to rise. As quickly as one rap of the staff, she was gone.

Three Sweaty Swans
JOHN LIBBY

Mr. Edgar stopped the pounding, and slowly the dancers wound down. Everyone sat, spent. The silence was as electric as the earlier din. Elijah was soaked in sweat, and euphoric. He watched Mr. Edgar turn with the staff, which now seemed smooth and straight, and walk slowly to the corner door. Elijah felt Mary's eyes and turned to her. She was also covered in perspiration. Elijah looked into her eyes; they were wet, loving, but more than that—knowing. She rushed to him and hugged him so hard it took his breath away. They did not speak. Slowly the people moved from the room, remaining quiet. The room's vitality began to subside. Mary and Elijah sat.

Mr. Edgar entered from his corner room and walked slowly up the aisle. He stopped, looking at Mary; she returned the look. Mr. Edgar smiled and turned his look to Elijah.

"You saw things?"

Mary jerked her head toward him.

"Oh, Eli. I saw you—I was looking up at you."

Elijah thought of the vision of her and the mask. As he began to speak, he saw the satisfied look on Mr. Edgar's face. Elijah, Mary and Mr. Edgar remained motionless and silent, aglow in the spirit of that meeting day.

▷─◁▷•─O─◁▷─◁

Dorothy
SANDRA L. MUDGE

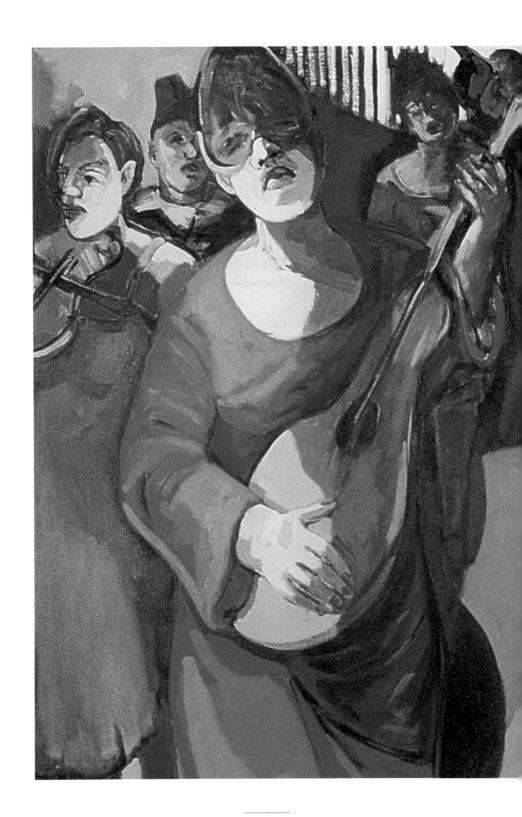

Capricchi
STEFANI JOSEPH

Ideas II
MOHAMED DANAWI

Overview
SANDRA REED

Silver Pendant
CHRISTOPHER MUNIZ

Untitled
CRAIG STEVENS

The Stylish Golfer
CATHERINE MYLER FRUISEN

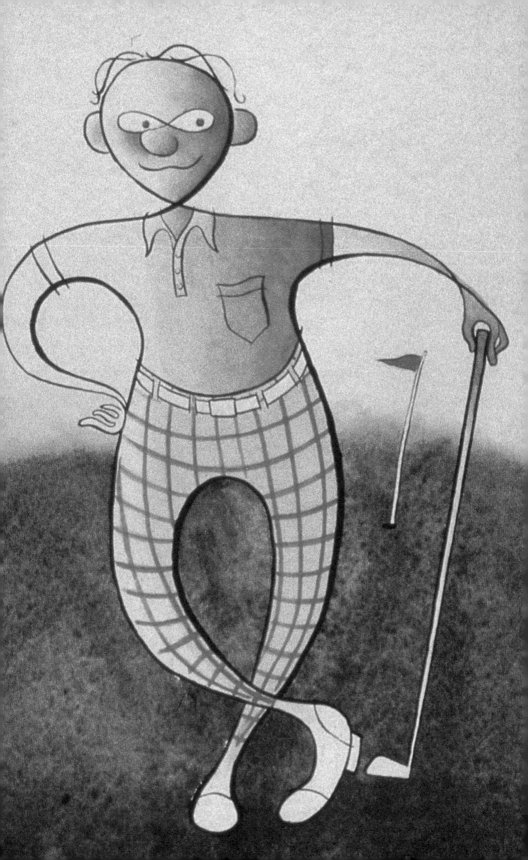

PARTNER

don't make me part of your personal play
or sew me into your fine fabric

I am not your mirror or coat
I am not your house or your air

my breath is not for running your machine
or cooling your neck

it's for breathing
back and forth
on wavelengths
stronger than ropes
or treads

just face me
eye to eye
hand to heart

see me
simply
as
another you

and together
we might weave
and build
and breathe
wide
open
fires

Untitled
PAUL HUDSON

MY YOUNG

Today I read about fishes called mouthbreeders
who carry their eggs and young in their mouths.

What a strange world it is,
who can tell me differently?

I who could not birth my children
only shelter them, long

to carry my young in this way,
palm them to mouth,

slip through the world with them
undetected until they are strong

enough, quick enough not to be eaten.
My girls, my young.

Untitled
PERNELL JOHNSON

SWIMMING LESSONS

The moon was scattered that night we were waiting. Standing just so in my driveway, you could see only bits of it between the last leaves, candles in dying hands.

It was a good night to be Out.

"So you're sure they can find this place?"

Lisa's sitting on my daddy's Vega, one leg up under her butt, looking for all the world like a high priestess for some local car ad. She did her hair differently tonight, pulled the too-long wings on either side of her face back with two pink barrettes shaped like mouths. My driveway's almost dark as a cave, though, and all you can see of Lisa is her new white Adidas (her daddy's the football coach), and the top of her new hairstyle that shines green under the sky. I can see that Adidas start up now, start kicking my daddy's fender. The Vega's nothing special, just a blue toadstool, but Daddy'd be mighty bent if he saw Lisa now.

"They're coming all right," I say assuredly, even though I'm starting to kick up gravel, getting the white dust all over my jeans. I'm starting to hate where we live, hate the weedy, tree-ridden land that we got so we'd never have to mow grass forever and ever, hate the white driveway that goes straight for what seems like miles, until you can see the old light of the street. I hate that we don't even have a mailbox, just a stake in the earth that bears three out of four of our street numbers, even though Daddy's forever buying those adhesive things that are never supposed to fall off. I hate having to explain all of this to friends.

A stalactite of light beams in the night, grows wider, then shuts. My mother stands on the doorstep. "Girls," she calls, "please come inside now. It's too cold to wait out here."

I can feel Lisa rolling around her made-up eyes. I can hear the soft thud she's making on the car with her Adidas. Please, just go *away*, make them come *now*. But there's more, as always.

Mama makes little crackles on the ground as she nears. She's wearing those little half-reading glasses, perched on her nose. They reflect like alien eyes in the moon.

She stops about five feet from me, peering into the driveway.

The Missed Communication
MARK UZMANN

"Do you think it's late enough," she asks, "to put away the candy?"

I blow through my mouth patiently. "Yes, Mom" (I always call her "Mom" when Lisa's around), "please go put away the candy."

But she's staring at me now, quite rudely, as if I were some newly purchased painting that displeased her. Her mind's a million miles away from little kids dressed as Batman.

"You two need to come inside," she says, swinging her head over to Lisa and then back to me, "now."

Lisa's so quiet she's practically screaming, and now I wish she would just go home, that my mother would disappear into the earth and be swallowed by naked molerats, that I could then fly through the half-dressed trees without a scratch.

Then so faintly, still blocks away, I hear the soft purr of a car. *Please....*

I exhale a cloud of milk in the night, feeling the jab of my mother's eyes for an acknowledgment. The purr's becoming a growl.

"Mom," I hiss, "they're coming, I hear them, all right, *already*?"

I am not allowed to talk to the Duchess like this, *ever*.

"Carolyn? I want you to come inside a minute—excuse us, Lisa—now. I want a coat over that—that—whatever that *outfit* is, and I think we need to have a little talk."

Lisa's off the car now. She hears the sound approaching and starts to shuffle toward the street. I *hate* her. I hope she *dies*. I hope she pours Nair on her blonde hair by accident and that her mother makes her go to school anyway. I hate it that my mother's not normal, that she wears those glasses and says things like "little talk." Even if Lisa doesn't tell anybody, she will still know. She with her football daddy coach and her new white shoes. I can already feel my hairspray unstick.

"Mama," I whisper, "they are coming. We can talk later."

Now she's about to call me: "Miss Surly. *If* you expect to go anywhere tonight—and at this rate it's looking dubious—you may go get a coat *with* me, and then you will explain to me who these boys are who seem to hold such an interest. You may also explain why you are going out so late, and you may give me the boys' parents' names."

Lisa greets the oncoming car, a horrifying spectacle pulling into our driveway.

Knowing I am not going to win this one unless I act crazy and deck my mother (ha!), I crunch fiercely behind her to the door, spilling sharp pieces of gravel into my shoe. The whole of the porch is aflame in headlights—Mama and I onstage!—as we approach the front door. I hear Lisa's harsh voice, revved up high Southern for flirting, fall like copper coins in the quiet night. God knows what she's saying.

"*Mama*," I whine, limping inside.

On the way home, the big moon rests atop pecan trees and casts light like honey over our faces. Gloria's mother is driving, but it feels more as if we're swimming, long and leisurely, through Route 16. No one lives this far away but me.... Gloria's mother is alone in the front seat. Her hair looks huge. I am amazed that she never turns that hair to look at us, not once. I have never met a mother like this. She doesn't even seem to have a benign curiosity, not an ounce of wonder, at the true fact that four people are squeezed into the backseat of the little car.

We are packed like this: girl-boy-boy-girl. I am the first girl, the one whose ear lies hotly inside Drew Norman's collar. The wool of his coat *smells* dark blue. He is still holding the same hand that twisted like a spider when he first took it, in the Haunted House. I wanted that hand back so I could hold my ears while we crept through the Mummy Hall, but then Drew would think I was weird, would spread it around that this girl holds her ears instead of closing her eyes or holding onto her man, who is a football *star*, no less. That would be worse than slow death by rabid remoras any day. So I'm glad now that I let my hand doze and grow warm in his, that we decided that Haunted Houses were cool, that I got scared and jumped so that Drew took my hand and held on.

I must love Drew, I think, and I yawn then, on Route 16, like I'm completely mellow and not jumping with thingies and ghouls all inside of me just like a real Haunted House, and also for Gloria's mother's sake, so she knows we're not *doing anything*. I keep forgetting she's not like a real mom.

But I'm feeling this—this *love* for Drew all over me, and I don't think I could sleep for years, even if I were paid money because my stomach's twisting harder than my hand ever did and I have this need to get on a swing and swing to the moon. I mean, I *have* to get on a swing, or something, because I'm feeling itchy and squirmy inside, and I'm smelling Drew's wool like it's the best new drug and I'm also embarrassed as get-out because *Gloria*, behind her *mother's* hair, is kissing Bobby so hard right next to us that it sounds like a balloon's being slowly squeezed out of air. I've never met a mother like this one. I hope, please God, that she never meets *mine*. I also wonder, while feeling queasy and itchy and weirdly good, what Lisa's mom is gonna think when Lisa doesn't come home with us, if I should write her an anonymous note saying that her sweet blonde daughter never went inside the House but took a walk with Scott Black instead. And that she didn't come back, not after two hours.

I bet she's going to Second Base right now.

We are nearing our turn and I'm glad cause the car's so hot and so quiet and Gloria's so loud and Bobby doesn't make a sound except for his leg that takes up most of the car and makes little squeaking noises near the bottom of the seat. Because of Bobby's leg, Drew had moved his own over the hump of the floor—else Bobby would be touching him— and squeezes them next to mine. I wonder, while desperately wanting to ride my bike straight to Jesus, if this hurts his—well, *you* know. The gray light of my subdivision, an island in a sea of cow grass, catches in the Big Hair at the wheel.

We are almost there. I am going to do cheerleader kicks 'til I nearly die. I am going to be in Deep Trouble because Mama will never believe that a mother brought me home this late, Gloria's moaning like a hyena and I wonder if she's drowning in Bobby's big lips. Drew is so quiet—something's wrong with me, that's it—the Tongue slides into my mouth so fast I don't have time to think.

Lights go out. Organs cease moving.

I do what I do next because I don't have time to think, because I don't understand that this is what we've been waiting for ever since the Mummy Hall and maybe before, that Gloria does this all the time and that Lisa does *more*....

All I know, swimming down that last street before my street, is that the biggest, saltiest, wettest *fish* has plunged into my mouth and is squirming deeper and deeper into my gullet.

So I bite.

I'm glad that I'm sick and don't go to school Monday. I don't even argue when Mama says it's because I stayed out so late, and didn't keep on my coat. Lisa didn't go to school either, so I call her after Mama leaves, and we spend two hours on the phone discussing Scott Black and this cheerleader outfit that's gotten too tight on her. When she asks if I French kissed with Drew, I tell her that's such a pretty word. She thinks it's weird that I would say that. When we hang up, I do about a thousand jumping jacks.

⊢┄◆┄◯┄◆┄┤

Sequence 8 from the
series "Usual Behavior"
Aya Mikami

LITTLE NIGHT BLUES

Full moon, fog-misty night.
Flourescent bar whiskey spouts
shining like towers of rose and gold
against the black nothingness
of what lies beyond.

Muted notes which will never
get any nearer to New York City
than a broken Dixieland dream.

Untitled
JOHN EARL

Untitled
JOHN EARL

IN GHASTLY VIEW

after Sonnet 27

Visible is a vibration of molecules, an agony,
the wearing away, the grinding of surface against
conspiring surface, of self looking on darkness
which the blind do see—the ether, in spite
of its failure to be, continues to circulate
to be felt in the small hours by those without telephones
or neighbors but sometimes by a quirk of time
in daylight the sound of some bird evokes
an echoing like longing like an echoing
response like light like reflected light
on the hull of the boat the waves slapping
and the spray rising into rainbows. Or
imagine the books of Braille powdering
under his very fingers as he reads again some
work that matters more.

Watermelons
TRACI HAYMANS

LEARNING HOW TO PRAY

When I heard my brother
was dying   youngest
of the six of us   our
lovely boy   I who in matters
of the spirit
had been always suspect
who even as a child
snubbed Mama's mealtime ritual
began finally to
pray   and fearing
I would offend
or miss completely
the rightful target of my pleas
went knocking everywhere
the Buddha's huge
and starry churning   Shiva
Vishnu   Isis   the worn
and ragged god of Ishmael
I bowed to the Druid reverence
of trees   to water   fire
and wind   prayed to weather
to carbon   that sole link
to all things
this and other worldly
our carbon who art in heaven
prayed to rake and plow
the sweet acid stench of dung
to fly   to the fly's soiled
wing   and to the soil
I could not stop
myself   I like a nymphomaniac
the dark promiscuity
of my spirit   there
for the taking   whore
of my breaking heart   willing
to lie down   with anything.

Untitled
BEN MORRIS

Untitled
CRAIG STEVENS

SLOW

I like the joke about the snail
who mugged the turtle
who when asked by the policeman
to recount the sequence of events
couldn't *because it all happened so fast.*

It's the only joke I know,
the one I always preface—*Stop me
if you've heard it*—though friends
who love me crack up each time, slap
each other on the back,
and laugh themselves to tears.

I want a life that slow.
Like George, the idiot savant,
who couldn't spell his name
or count to ten, but could remember
for the talk-show host, the weather
of any day she named—her high school
graduation, Pearl Harbor,
the day the Rosenbergs were killed.

I'll tell you the truth, he would begin,
the year washing slowly back, cresting,
sweet wave against his tongue,
the little ark of months and days
come to rest on Ararat. *June 7, 1959.*
Warm and sunny that one was, and then,
the wreck of his old hand rising toward the sky,
The truth I've told will get me into heaven.

I want a life that slow. To lumber
each morning out of the slush
and mire, my earthly possessions
strapped across my spine. And like
George, famous for making small-talk
I'll turn to you, good friend, idling
on the stump next door, the wound-down
clock of your body glistening in the light,

and *Stop me if you've heard this,* I'll begin,
as your eyes bank with tears, happy
with this old joke, this weather
this truth I've told, again.

Delphic
KATHERINE SANDOZ

Ogeechee Canal
LORI L. JOHNSON

Currency of Information
PAMELA WILEY

THE AUTHORS

Lisa Bahlinger is a freelance editor and poet who lives in Stone Mountain, Georgia. She has edited numerous stories for SCAD's Design Press.

Cathy Smith Bowers is poet in residence at Queens College in Charlotte, North Carolina. Her poems have appeared widely in prestigious journals. She also has published three books of poetry. During 1999, she visited SCAD under the auspices of the Georgia Poetry Circuit.

Scott Boylston is a professor of graphic design at SCAD. He has published numerous short stories and is currently finishing a book on graphic design.

John Earl is a professor in the liberal arts department at SCAD. He teaches the history of jazz and is an award-winning nature photographer.

Martha Furlong is a professor of poetry at SCAD. She also directs the new writing minor program. Her poems have appeared in numerous journals.

Elizabeth Hudson-Goff is a freelance editor and writer. She was previously employed as an editor at SCAD.

Marilyn Nelson is a professor of English at the University of Connecticut at Storrs. Published widely in influential journals, she is also the author of five books of poetry. She visited SCAD during 2000 under the auspices of the Georgia Poetry Circuit.

Bin Ramke is editor of the *Denver Quarterly* and the Contemporary Poetry Series. He teaches in the creative writing program at the University of Denver and is the author of five books of poetry. He visited SCAD during 2000 under the auspices of the Georgia Poetry Circuit.

Lew Tate is a professor of English at SCAD. His work has appeared in *The Georgia Guardian* and other publications.

Becky Wible is chair of the computer art department at SCAD. She came to Savannah from New York City, where she owned a clay and stop-motion animation company.

George Williams is a professor of creative writing at SCAD. His short stories have appeared in numerous publications, and he is the recipient of two Pushcart awards.

THE EDITORS

Teresa Griffis is a professor of English and former chair of the liberal arts department at SCAD. Her poetry and essays have appeared in several publications.

John Valentine is a professor of philosophy at SCAD. His poetry has appeared in the *International Review of Poetry*, *Chiron Review* and other journals.

Elethia Oliver Ajose received an M.F.A. from SCAD in 1995. She teaches part-time at East Carolina University and is active in creating and exhibiting her artwork.

Steve Bliss is a professor of photography at SCAD. His work has appeared in numerous shows and exhibitions.

Pete Christman is a professor of photography at SCAD. He is a commercial photographer and painter whose work has appeared in numerous shows and venues.

Mohamed Danawi is a professor of illustration and chair of the illustration department at SCAD. He has won several regional and national awards and is currently working on a children's book for Design Press.

Shelley Davis received an M.F.A. from SCAD in 2000. Her current projects involve working in mixed media and photography.

Larry Dixon is a professor of photography at SCAD. He has shown his work at the national and international levels.

Denise Falk is a professor of painting at SCAD. Her works have appeared in many shows, and she is well known both nationally and internationally.

Joy L. Flynn is a professor in the foundation department at SCAD. She has won numerous awards, including an ad for Absolut Vodka, and continues to exhibit nationally.

Catherine Myler Fruisen is a professor of illustration at SCAD. She has been a costume and scenic designer in New York City and has recently illustrated three children's books in conjunction with Design Press.

Traci Haymans is a professor in the illustration department at SCAD. She is a freelance illustrator who works for various magazines and publishers.

Jon O. Holloway received an M.F.A. from SCAD in 1996. He is a freelance photographer in Greenwood, South Carolina.

Paul Hudson is a professor in the sequential art department at SCAD. His work has earned national and international acclaim.

Henry Pernell Johnson is a professor in the foundation department at SCAD. His work has appeared in a variety of exhibits.

Lori L. Johnson received an M.F.A. from SCAD in 2000. She lives in Jacksonville, Florida, where she continues to produce and exhibit her work.

Stefani Joseph is a professor in the foundation department at SCAD. She is a well-known artist whose work has appeared in various national and international shows.

Dick Krepel is a professor of illustration at SCAD. He has illustrated on a national level for the past twenty years, winning numerous regional and national awards.

John Libby received an M.F.A. from SCAD in 1996. He is a senior illustrator/art director for an analyst firm in Nashua, New Hampshire.

Winslett Long received an M.F.A. from SCAD in 2000. She is associate designer for Design Press.

Tara McKiernan received an M.F.A. from SCAD in 2000. She is currently living and working in Connecticut.

Aya Mikami received an M.F.A. from SCAD in 1997. She is currently a project manager for a design firm in San Francisco.

Ben Morris (1930-1998) taught at SCAD for thirteen years. A flexible faculty member, he taught in the fashion, illustration, interior design, textile design, and foundation departments, and was instrumental in establishing the fashion program at the college. Prior to coming to SCAD, Morris was a fashion illustrator for Hubert Givenchy and Lily Daché, and illustrated for publications including the *New York Times*, *Harper's Bazaar* and *Vogue*, and was an illustrator/reporter for *Women's Wear Daily*.

Sandra Mudge received an M.F.A. from SCAD in 2000. She is employed as a staff photographer at the *Georgia Guardian*.

Christopher Muniz received his B.F.A. from SCAD in 1996. He is an exhibit designer at the J. Paul Getty Museum in Los Angeles, California.

Sandra Reed is a professor of painting and chair of the painting department at SCAD. She received an M.F.A. from the George Washington University and has exhibited her work in many national venues.

Paul Sabo received an B.F.A. from SCAD in 1998. He lives in San Francisco where he is a shipping/purchasing manager for Thomas-Swan Sign Company. He also is a part-time photography instructor at San Francisco Photo Center.

Katherine Sandoz is a professor of illustration at SCAD and art director of the Gallery at Cafe Metropole. She recently exhibited her work in Switzerland.

Craig Stevens is a professor of photography and chair of the photography department at SCAD. His work has earned acclaim both nationally and internationally and is featured in many museums and shows.

Tongjit Tieophanitjaroen received an M.F.A. from SCAD in 1999. She is a scenic artist at Sightline Studios in Florida.

Mark Uzmann is a professor of psychology in the liberal arts department at SCAD. He is also an award-winning photographer.

Pamela Wiley is a professor of fibers at SCAD. She received her graduate degree at Cranbrook Academy of Art and works in fibers, designing textiles and creating props for Broadway shows.

The goal of the Savannah College of Art and Design is to nurture and cultivate the unique qualities of each student through an interesting curriculum, in an inspiring environment, under the leadership of involved professors. The college exists to prepare talented students for careers in the visual and performing arts, design, building arts, and the history of art and architecture. The college emphasizes individual attention in a positively oriented environment.

The Savannah College of Art and Design is a private, non-profit, accredited college awarding bachelor of architecture, bachelor of fine arts, master of architecture, master of arts and master of fine arts degrees. The college offers 18 major areas of study: architectural history, architecture, art history, computer art, fashion, fibers, furniture design, graphic design, historic preservation, illustration, interior design, media and performing arts, metals and jewelry, painting, photography, product design, sequential art, and video/film. Minors are offered in each of the major programs as well as in decorative arts, drawing, electronic design, museum studies, printmaking, sculpture, sound design and writing.

Class size is small, allowing each student the opportunity to receive individual attention. Each professor is uniquely qualified—professionally and educationally—in his or her field. The international faculty and student body have come from each of the 50 states and from 80 countries. The learning atmosphere available to students is friendly, open and challenging. A strong English as a Second Language program is offered, and professional staff are dedicated to assisting international students with their adjustment to college life in the United States.

The facilities of the college provide leading-edge technology in a historic setting. College buildings are characterized by turrets, bell towers, balconies, and elaborate wrought iron, and feature dramatic staircases, skylights, decorative molding, and large, airy spaces.

The college is a leader in restoring architectural treasures in

Savannah's renowned National Historic Landmark District, winning recognition from the Historic Savannah Foundation, the Georgia Trust for Historic Preservation, the Art Deco Societies of America, the National Trust for Historic Preservation, the American Institute of Architects and the International Downtown Association.

The meteoric growth of the college from 71 students at its opening in 1979 to more than 4,500 students today has brought culture, vitality and a tremendous economic boost to the Savannah community. Many graduates have chosen to remain in the area to work in design or architectural firms or to start their own businesses.

The campus includes more than 40 facilities equipped with the latest technology available. Among these facilities are numerous structures that were once important public buildings. Having outlived their original 19th century purposes, many of these architectural treasures had become abandoned eyesores. Restored or renovated by the college, the buildings have been adapted to new educational and administrative uses. Students have access to classrooms, studios, an extensive art and architecture library, computer labs, darkrooms, processing labs, and editing and postproduction suites. An art supply and book store, restaurants, and galleries are conveniently located throughout the campus. The college also provides a fitness center and a minor illness clinic, as well as a selection of residence halls.

The Savannah College of Art and Design competes at the NCAA Division III level in baseball, basketball, cross country, equestrian, golf, rowing, soccer, softball, tennis and volleyball. The college sponsors a cheerleading squad and dance line, as well as a variety of intramural sports.

For more information about the college, programs of study, or cultural events the college sponsors, call 800.869.7223 or visit the college on the World Wide Web at http://www.scad.edu. Admission inquiries may be sent to admissions@scad.edu. Other requests may be directed to info@scad.edu.